BMA Board of Science

Editorial board

A publication from the BMA Science & Education departme

British Library Cataloguing-in-Publication Data.
A catalogue record for this book is available from the British Library.

ISBN: 1-905545-11-8

Cover photograph: Getty Images Creative
Printed by British Medical Association

Board of Science

This report was prepared under the auspices of the Board of Science of the British Medical Association, whose membership for 2006/07 was as follows:

Professor Parveen Kumar CBE — President, BMA
Dr Michael Wilks — Chair, BMA Representative Body
Mr James N Johnson — Chair, BMA Council
Dr David Pickersgill — Treasurer, BMA
Sir Charles George — Chair, Board of Science
Dr P B Maguire — Deputy Chair, Board of Science
Dr P H Dangerfield
Dr G D Dilliway
Dr G D Lewis
Dr S Minkoff
Dr O Moghraby
Dr G Rae
Dr D M Sinclair
Dr A S Thomson
Dr D M B Ward
Dr D G Wrigley
Dr C Spencer-Jones (by invitation)
Dr S Chaudhry (Co-optee)
Dr E F Coyle (Co-optee)
Dr P Steadman (Co-optee)
Dr S J Nelson (Deputy member)

Approval for publication as a BMA policy report was recommended by BMA Board of Professional Activities on 1 December 2006.

> **Declaration of interest**
> There were no competing interests with any Board member involved in the research and writing of this report. For further information about the editorial secretariat or Board members please contact the Science and Education Department which holds a record of all declarations of interest: info.science@bma.org.uk

About the contributing author

Professor Mark Griffiths is a Chartered Psychologist and Director of the International Gaming Research Unit (IGRU) at Nottingham Trent University. The IGRU is the UK's largest gambling research unit and conducts research in the area of gaming, risk taking and interactive technologies. Professor Griffiths is Europe's only Professor of Gambling Studies and has researched and written widely on gambling and gambling addictions. He has received seven national and international awards for his gambling research including the US **John Rosecrance Research Prize** for 'outstanding scholarly contributions to the field of gambling research' (1994), the Spanish **CELEJ Prize** for best paper on gambling (1998), the Canadian **International Excellence Award** for 'the extraordinary contribution made to problem gambling over many years' (2003) and the North American **Lifetime Achievement Award For Contributions To The Field Of Youth Gambling** 'in recognition of his dedication, leadership, and pioneering contributions to the field of youth gambling' (2006).

Acknowledgements

The association is very grateful for the help provided by the BMA committees and many outside experts and organisations. We would particularly like to thank Dr Gerda Reith, Senior Lecturer, Department of Sociology, Anthropology and Applied Social Sciences, University of Glasgow.

Abbreviations

BGPS	British Gambling Prevalence Survey
DCMS	Department for Culture, Media and Sport
DH	Department of Health
DSM	Diagnostic and Statistical Manual of Mental Disorders
EGM	Electronic Gaming Machine
IGRI	International Gaming Research Unit
PGSI	Problem Gambling Severity Index
RIGT	Responsibility in Gambling Trust
SOGS	South Oaks Gambling Screen

Foreword

At the BMA's 2006 annual representative meeting a resolution on gambling addiction and its treatment in the NHS was referred to the Board of Science. In addressing this resolution, the Board of Science decided to undertake a review of what services are available in the United Kingdom (UK) for problem gamblers and who provides them, and establish what (if any) treatment and prevention services are available on the NHS for gambling addiction in order to raise awareness of the problem in the UK.

The report is aimed at healthcare professionals, policy makers and service providers, and makes recommendations for tackling this growing problem in the UK. The forthcoming implementation of the Gambling Act 2005 will have important implications for gambling in the UK, potentially facilitating an increase in problem gambling. It is therefore important for healthcare professionals, policy makers and service providers to be aware of these developments in order to respond appropriately to a likely increase in demand for gambling addiction treatment.

Professor Sir Charles George
Chair, Board of Science

The Board of Science, a standing committee of the BMA, provides an interface between the medical profession, the government and the public. The board produces numerous reports containing policies for national action by government and other organisations, with specific recommendations affecting the medical and allied professions.

Contents

Introduction

On 18 October 2004 a Gambling Bill was introduced into Parliament. Following consideration by the House of Commons and the House of Lords, it received Royal Assent on 7 April 2005, and became the Gambling Act 2005. The initial target for full implementation of the Act is 1 September 2007. It has been recognised that the introduction of this new legislation may have important implications for public health through changing patterns of gambling and hence rates of problem gambling (Griffiths, 2004). It is important that healthcare professionals are aware of these developments in order that they may respond appropriately to a potential increase in demand for gambling addiction treatment.

Gambling is a popular activity and recent national surveys into gambling participation (including the National Lottery), show that over 70 per cent of adults gamble annually (Sproston, Erens & Orford, 2000; Creigh-Tyte & Lepper, 2004). Gambling also makes a significant contribution to the economy: in the year ending 31 March 2004 gambling expenditure was estimated at £8.875bn, which corresponds to 0.8 per cent of the UK GDP (Ward, 2004). This expenditure was used to pay £1.3bn in gambling-related duties (approximately 0.3% of total government revenues), and around £1.3bn in good causes contributions. The gaming machine sector is the most profitable branch of the industry (accounting for some 70% of government revenue) (Ward, 2004).

Although most people gamble occasionally for fun and pleasure, gambling brings with it inherent risks of personal and social harm. According to research commissioned by *GamCare* (a non-government organisation (NGO) that provides treatment, education and research on problem gambling) and conducted by an independent research company, the National Centre for Social Research, there are approximately 300,000 problem gamblers in the UK which equates to just under 1 per cent of the adult population (Sproston et al, 2000). Problem gambling can negatively affect significant areas of a person's life, including their physical and mental health, employment, finances and interpersonal relationships (eg family members, financial dependents) (Griffiths, 2004). There are significant co-morbidities with problem gambling, including depression, alcoholism, and obsessive-compulsive behaviours. These co-morbidities may exacerbate, or be exacerbated by, problem gambling. Availability of opportunities to gamble and the incidence of problem gambling within a community are known to be linked (Griffiths, 2003a; Abbott & Volberg, in press). A review of the accessibility and availability of gambling addiction services, as well as raising awareness among general practitioners (GPs) and other healthcare workers of these services and other relevant treatments, is therefore essential as the target date for full implementation of the Gambling Act 2005 draws near.

Problem gambling

Definition of gambling

Gambling is a diverse concept that incorporates a range of activities undertaken in a variety of settings. It includes differing sets of behaviours and perceptions among participants and observers (Abbott & Volberg, 1999). Predominantly, gambling has an economic meaning and usually refers to risking (or wagering) money or valuables on the outcome of a game, contest, or other event in the hope of winning additional money or material goods. The activity varies on several dimensions, including what is being wagered, how much is being wagered, the expected outcome, and the predictability of the event. For some things such as lotteries, most slot machines and bingo, the results are random and unpredictable. For other things, such as sports betting and horse racing, there is some predictability to the outcome and the use of skills and knowledge (eg recent form, environmental factors) can give a person an advantage over other gamblers. Some of the UK's most common types of offline commercial forms of gambling are summarised in box 1.

Box 1: A summary of the most common forms of offline commercial gambling in the UK

Type of gambling	Brief description
The National Lottery	National lottery game where players pick six out of 49 numbers to be drawn bi-weekly for the chance to win a large prize. Tickets can be bought from a wide variety of outlets including supermarkets, newsagents or petrol stations.
Bingo	A game of chance where randomly selected numbers are drawn and players match those numbers to those appearing on pre-bought cards. The first person to have a card where the drawn numbers form a specified pattern is the winner. Usually played in bingo halls but can be played in amusement arcades and other settings (eg church hall).
Card games (eg poker, bridge, blackjack)	Gambling while playing card games either privately (eg with friends) or in commercial settings (eg land-based casino) in an attempt to win money.
Sports betting	Wagering of money for example on horse races, greyhound races or football matches. Usually in a betting shop in an attempt to win money.
Non-sports betting	Wagering of money on a non-sporting event (such as who will be evicted from the 'Big Brother' house) usually done in a betting shop in an attempt to win money.
Scratchcards	Instant win games where players typically try to match a number of winning symbols to win prizes. These can be bought in the same types of outlet as the National Lottery.
Roulette	Game in which players try to predict where a spinning ball will land on a 36-numbered wheel. This game can be played with a real roulette wheel (eg in a casino) or on electronic gaming machines (eg in a betting shop).
Gaming machines (eg fruit machines, fixed odds betting terminals)	These are stand-alone electronic gaming machines that come in a variety of guises. These include many different types of 'fruit machine' (typically played in amusement arcades, family leisure centres, casinos, etc) and fixed odds betting terminals (FOBTs) typically played in betting shops.
Football pools	Weekly game in which players try to predict which football games will end in a score draw for the chance of winning a big prize. Game is typically played via door-to-door agents.
Spread betting	Relatively new form of gambling where players try to predict the 'spread' of a particular sporting activity, such as the number of runs scored in a cricket match or the exact time of the first goal in a football match, in an attempt to win money. Players use a spread betting agency (a type of specialised bookmaker).

(Notes on box 1: [1] Most of these forms of gambling can now be done via other gambling channels including the internet, interactive television and/or mobile phone. [2] There are other types of gambling such as dice (casino-based 'craps'), keno (a fast draw lottery game) and video lottery terminal machines. However, these are either unavailable or very rare in the UK. [3] Technically, activities such as speculation on the stock market or day trading are types of gambling but these are not typically viewed as commercial forms of gambling and they are not taxed in the same way.)

As can be seen from box 1, gambling is commonly undertaken in a variety of environments including those dedicated primarily to gambling (eg betting shops, casinos, bingo halls, amusement arcades), those where gambling is peripheral to other activities (eg social clubs, pubs, sports venues), and those environments where gambling is just one of many things that can be done (eg supermarkets, post offices or petrol stations). In addition, most types of gambling can now be engaged in remotely via the internet, interactive television and/or mobile phone. This includes playing roulette or slot machines at an online casino, the buying of lottery tickets using a mobile phone or betting on a horse race using interactive television. In these remote types of gambling, players use their credit cards, debit cards or other electronic forms of money to deposit funds in order to gamble (Griffiths, 2005a). Concerns surrounding remote gambling will be examined later in this report.

Definition of terms

In the UK, the term 'problem gambling' has been used by many researchers, bodies, and organisations, to describe gambling that compromises, disrupts or damages family, employment, personal or recreational pursuits (Budd Commission, 2001; Sproston et al, 2000; Griffiths, 2004; Responsibility in Gambling Trust). The two most widely used screening instruments worldwide are the Diagnostic and Statistical Manual of Mental Disorders, fourth edition (DSM-IV) for pathological gambling (American Psychiatric Association, 1994), and the South Oaks Gambling Screen (SOGS) (Lesieur & Blume, 1987). Both screening instruments were used to measure problem gambling in the British Gambling Prevalence Survey (BGPS). Further, these two screening tools are the most widely used by UK researchers and other UK service providers in patient consultations (eg *GamCare*). The screens are based on instruments used for diagnostic purposes in clinical settings, and are designed for use in the general population (Sproston et al, 2000).

There is some disagreement in the literature as to the terminology used, as well as the most appropriate screens to diagnose and measure the phenomenon. Researchers internationally are beginning to reach a consensus over a view of problem gambling that moves away from earlier, often heavily DSM-based clinical definitions. For instance, early conceptions of 'pathological gambling' were of a discrete 'disease entity' comprising a chronic, progressive mental illness, which only complete abstinence could hope to manage. More recent thinking regards problem gambling as behaviour that exists on a continuum, with extreme, pathological presentation at one end, very minor problems at the other, and a range of more or less disruptive behaviours in between. Moreover, this behaviour is something that is mutable. Research suggests it can change over time as individuals move in and out of problematic status and is often subject to natural remission (Hayer, Meyer & Griffiths, 2005). Put more simply, gamblers can often move back to non-problematic recreational playing after spells of even quite serious problems. This conception fits in with an emphasis on more general public health, with a focus on the social, personal and physical 'harms' that gambling problems can create among various sectors of the population, rather than a more narrow focus on the psychological and/or psychiatric problems of a minority of 'pathological' individuals. Such a focus tends also to widen the net to encompass a range of problematic behaviours that can affect much larger sections of the population.

The screening tools that are currently used to diagnose the existence and severity of problem gambling reflect this change of focus. There have been criticisms of both the DSM-IV and the SOGS. In part, these criticisms stem from an acknowledgment that both screens were designed for use in clinical settings, and not among the general population, within which large numbers of individuals with varying degrees of problems reside. A range of alternative screening instruments have been developed, and these are increasingly being used internationally (Abbott, Volberg, Bellringer & Reith, 2004). One such screening tool is the Problem Gambling Severity Index (PGSI), which was developed in Canada and has been used in the UK, the USA and Australia. This screen will replace the SOGS in the upcoming BGPS. This survey will provide comprehensive data on the prevalence and distribution of problem gambling in this country. It will therefore be useful for practitioners to have some understanding of the types of screening tools it will use, as well as the different orientations that lie behind them.

A 'harm based' conception of problem gambling has implications for policy and treatment. Given that the most severe cases of pathological gambling are one of the most difficult disorders to treat (Volberg, 1996), and given that, at various points in their lives, members of the general population may experience some degree of gambling-related harms, it becomes important to provide intervention strategies that can prevent this potential group developing more serious problems. To this end, public health education and awareness-raising initiatives come to the fore, and these are recognised internationally as the most cost-effective way of dealing with problem gambling in the long term (Shaffer, Hall & Vander Bilt, 1999; Abbott et al, 2004; National Gambling Impact Study Commission, 1999). Such strategies have been successfully deployed in countries such as Australia, New Zealand and Canada.

There is a multitude of terms used to refer to individuals who experience difficulties related to their gambling. These reflect the differing aims and emphases among various stakeholders concerned with treating patients, studying the phenomenon, and influencing public policy in relation to gambling legislation. Besides 'problem' gambling, terms include (but are not limited to) 'pathological', 'addictive', 'excessive', 'dependent', 'compulsive', 'impulsive', 'disordered', and 'at-risk' (Griffiths & Delfabbro, 2001; Griffiths, 2006). Terms are also employed to reflect more precisely the differing severities of addiction. For example, 'moderate' can refer to a lesser level of problem, and 'serious problem gambling' to the more severe end of the spectrum.

Although there is no absolute agreement, commonly 'problem gambling' is used as a general term to indicate all of the patterns of disruptive or damaging gambling behaviour. This report follows this precedent, employing the use of the term 'problem gambling' to refer to the broad spectrum of gambling-related problems. Problem gambling must be distinguished from social gambling and professional gambling. Social gambling typically occurs with friends or colleagues and lasts for a limited period of time, with predetermined acceptable losses. There are also those who gamble alone in a non-problematic way without any social component. In professional gambling, risks are limited and discipline is central. Some individuals can experience problems associated with their gambling, such as loss of control and short-term chasing behaviour (whereby the individual attempts to recoup their losses), that do not meet the full criteria for pathological gambling (American Psychiatric Association, 1994).

Social context

Research into gambling practices, the prevalence of problem gambling, and the socio-demographic variables associated with gambling and problem gambling, has not been considered part of mainstream health research agendas until quite recently. The BGPS (Sproston et al, 2000) was the first nationally representative survey of its kind conducted in Britain. The extent of gambling activity, as measured in the survey, revealed gambling to be a popular activity in Britain. In the year covered by the survey, gambling was engaged in by almost three-quarters of the population (72%), with the most popular gambling activity being the National Lottery Draw (ie Lotto). Two-thirds of the population bought a National Lottery ticket in the year covered by the survey (65%), while the next most popular gambling activity was the purchase of scratchcards (22%), followed by playing fruit machines (14%), horse race gambling (13%), football pools (9%) and bingo (7%). For a large number of people (39% of those who purchased National Lottery tickets), the National

Lottery Lotto game was the only gambling activity they participated in.

The BGPS also found that men were more likely than women to gamble (76% of men and 68% of women gambled in the year covered by the survey), and tended to stake more money on gambling activities. The gambling activities men and women participated in were also varied. Men were more likely to play football pools and fruit machines, bet on horse and dog races, and to make private bets with friends, while women were more likely to play bingo, and tended to participate in a lesser number of gambling activities overall (Sproston et al, 2000).

There are also cultural variations in the prevalence and type of gambling activities. For instance, in other cultures there is greater participation in games like PaiGow[1] and dice, or betting on cockfights. The type of gambling activity engaged in also differs according to social class. Although gambling is popular among people of all social classes, people in social class I are more likely to go to casinos (5%) than play bingo (3%), while the opposite is true among people in social class V, who have a participation rate of 20 per cent in bingo, and only 1 per cent in casinos. Income is a factor in gambling participation, with people living in low-income households (under £10,400) being the least likely to gamble. In general, participation in gambling activities tends to increase along with household income until around the level of £36,000, after which participation rates level off and decline slightly (Sproston et al, 2000). However, it must be noted that those in the lower classes spending the same amount on gambling as those in higher social classes will be spending a disproportionately higher amount of disposable income on gambling.

Examination of prevalence and socio-demographic variables associated with problem gambling undertaken in the BGPS revealed that between 0.6 per cent and 0.8 per cent (275,000 to 370,000 people) of the population aged 16 and over were problem gamblers (Sproston et al, 2000). In comparison to other countries (such as Australia, the USA, New Zealand and Spain which have problem gambling rates of 2.3, 1.1, 1.2 and 1.4% respectively), the number of problem gamblers in Britain is – based on the 2000 prevalence survey – relatively low (Sproston et al, 2000).

Profiling

The BGPS revealed that there were a number of socio-demographic factors statistically associated with problem gambling. These included being male, having a parent who was or who has been a problem gambler, being separated or divorced and having a low income. Low income is one of the most consistent factors associated with problem gambling worldwide. This may be both a cause and an effect. Being on a low income may be a reason to gamble in the first place (ie to try to win money). Additionally, gambling may lead to low income as a result of consistent losing. In Britain, people in the lowest income categories are three times more likely to be classed a problem gambler than average (Sproston et al, 2000). Although many people on low incomes may not spend more on gambling, in absolute terms, than those on higher wages, they do spend a much greater proportion of their incomes than these groups. The links with general 'disadvantage' should also be noted. Research shows that those who experience unemployment, poor health and housing, and low educational qualifications have significantly higher rates of problem gambling than the general population (Griffiths & Delfabbro, 2001; Griffiths, 2006).

---

1   PaiGow is a Chinese gambling game that is played with Chinese domino tiles. http://www.paigow.com

The American Psychiatric Association (1994) claims that approximately one third of problem gamblers are women. In the USA this loosely corroborates the results of the BGPS that showed that approximately 1.3 per cent of men and 0.5 per cent of women in Britain could be classified as problem gamblers (Sposton et al, 2000). Results of the BGPS also showed that the prevalence of problem gambling decreased with age. For instance, the prevalence of problem gambling was 1.7 per cent among people aged between 16 and 24, but only 0.1 per cent among the oldest age group. Further, the prevalence was highest among men and women aged between 16 and 24 (2.3% and 1.1% respectively).

The types of games played also impact on the development of gambling problems. This has consequences for understanding the risk factors involved in the disorder, as well as the demographic profile of those individuals who are most susceptible. For instance, certain features of games are strongly associated with problem gambling. These include games that have a high event frequency (ie that are fast and allow for continual staking), that involve an element of skill or perceived skill, and that create 'near misses' (ie the illusion of having almost won) (Griffiths, 1999). Size of jackpot and stakes, probability of winning (or perceived probability of winning), and the possibility of using credit to play are also associated with higher levels of problematic play (Parke & Griffiths, 2006; in press). Games that meet these criteria include electronic gaming machines (EGMs) and casino table games.

According to the BGPS, the most problematic type of gambling in Britain is associated with games in a casino (8.7% of people who gambled on this activity in the past year were problem gamblers according to the SOGS, and 5.6% according to the DSM-IV). Groups most likely to experience problems with casino-based gambling were single, unemployed males, aged under 30. Other subgroups include slightly older single males, aged over 40, often retired, who are also more likely to be of Chinese ethnicity (Fisher, 2000), and adolescent males who have problems particularly with fruit machines (Griffiths, 1995; 2002). The problem of adolescent gambling will be examined in more detail later in this report.

The BGPS also indicated that other types of gambling activities were engaged in by problem gamblers. These included betting on events with a bookmaker (SOGS 8.1%; DSM-IV 5.8%), and betting on dog races (SOGS 7.2%; DSM-IV 3.7%). Problem gamblers were less likely to participate in the National Lottery (1.2% of people who gambled on this activity in the past year were problem gamblers according to the SOGS; 0.7% according to the DSM-IV), or playing scratchcards (SOGS 1.7%; DSM-IV 1.5%). In addition, problem gambling prevalence was associated with the number of gambling activities undertaken, with the prevalence of problem gambling tending to increase with the number of gambling activities participated in. As noted above, for a large number of people, the National Lottery was the only gambling activity they engaged in, and problem gambling prevalence among people who limit their gambling to activities such as the National Lottery and scratchcards was very low at 0.1 per cent. As might be expected, problem gambling was associated with higher expenditure on gambling activities.

Internationally, as in almost every other country worldwide, the greatest problems are, to a very considerable degree, associated with non-casino EGMs such as arcade 'fruit machines' (Griffiths, 1999; Parke & Griffiths, 2006). It has been found that as EGMs spread, they tend to displace almost every other type of gambling as well as the problems that are associated with them. EGMs are the fastest-growing sector of the gaming economy, currently accounting for some 70 per cent of revenue. Australia's particularly high rates of problem gambling are almost entirely accounted for by its high density of these non-casino machines. It is likely that Britain's relatively lower rates of problems associated with EGMs is explained by its current legislative environment, which limits the numbers of machines in what are relatively regulated venues. This situation will change however, as the Gambling Act 2005 comes into force, allowing larger numbers of higher stakes machines into casinos, bingo halls and other gambling venues. All of this indicates that attention should be focused on EGMs as a source of risk.

The spread of EGMs also impacts on the demographic groups who experience problems with gambling. Until very recently, such problems were predominantly found in males, but as EGMs proliferate, women are increasingly presenting in greater numbers, so that in some countries (eg the USA), the numbers are almost equal. This trend has been described as a 'feminisation' of problem gambling (Volberg, 2001). These types of games appear to be particularly attractive to recent migrants, who are also at high risk of developing gambling problems.[2] It has been suggested that first generation migrants may not be sufficiently socially, culturally or even financially adapted to their new environment to protect them from the potential risks of excessive gambling (Productivity Commission, 1999; Shaffer, LaBrie & LaPlante, 2004). Many are therefore vulnerable to the development of problems. This highlights the need for healthcare professionals to be aware of the specific groups – increasingly, women and new migrants, as well as young males and adolescents – who may present with gambling problems which may or may not be masked by other symptoms.

Variations in gambling preferences are thought to result from both differences in accessibility and motivation. Older people tend to choose activities that minimise the need for complex decision-making or concentration (eg bingo, slot machines), whereas gender differences have been attributed to a number of factors, including variations in sex-role socialisation, cultural differences and theories of motivation (Griffiths, 2006). Variations in motivation are also frequently observed among people who participate in the same gambling activity. For example, slot machine players may gamble to win money, for enjoyment and excitement, to socialise and to escape negative feelings (Griffiths, 1995). Some people gamble for one reason only, whereas others gamble for a variety of reasons. A further complexity is that people's motivations for gambling have a strong temporal dimension; that is, they do not remain stable over time. As people progress from social to regular and finally to excessive gambling, there are often significant changes in their reasons for gambling. Whereas a person might have initially gambled to obtain enjoyment, excitement and socialisation, the progression to problem gambling is almost always accompanied by an increased preoccupation with winning money and chasing losses.

Youth gambling

Adolescent gambling is a cause for concern in the UK and is related to other delinquent behaviours. For instance, in one study of over 4,500 adolescents, gambling was highly correlated with other potentially addictive activities such as illicit drug taking and alcohol abuse (Griffiths & Sutherland, 1998). Another study by Yeoman and Griffiths (1996) demonstrated that around 4 per cent of all juvenile crime in one UK city was slot machine-related, based on over 1,850 arrests in a one-year period. It has also been noted that adolescents may be more susceptible to problem gambling than adults. For instance, in the UK, a number of studies have consistently highlighted a figure of up to 5 to 6 per cent of pathological gamblers among adolescent fruit machine gamblers (see Griffiths, [2002; 2003b] for an overview of these studies). This figure is at least two to three times higher than that identified in adult populations. On this evidence, young people are clearly

---

2   Research as to whether this applies to all migrant groups is not available. Most of this field has been dominated by studies of Hispanic migration in the USA and studies of indigenous groups in Australia and New Zealand, but there have not yet been cross-cultural comparisons.

more vulnerable to the negative consequences of gambling than adults.

A typical finding of many adolescent gambling studies has been that problem gambling appears to be a primarily male phenomenon. It also appears that adults may to some extent be fostering adolescent gambling. For example, a strong correlation has been found between adolescent gambling and parental gambling (Wood & Griffiths, 1998; 2004). This is particularly worrying because a number of studies have shown that individuals who gamble as adolescents, are then more likely to become problem gamblers as adults (Griffiths, 2003b). Similarly, many studies have indicated a strong link between adult problem gamblers and later problem gambling among their children (Griffiths, 2003b). Other factors that have been linked with adolescent problem gambling include working class youth culture, delinquency, alcohol and substance abuse, poor school performance, theft and truancy (Griffiths, 1995; Yeoman & Griffiths, 1996; Griffiths & Sutherland, 1998).

The main form of problem gambling among adolescents has been the playing of fruit machines. There is little doubt that fruit machines are potentially 'addictive' and there is now a large body of research worldwide supporting this. Most research on fruit machine gambling in youth has been undertaken in the UK where they are legally available to children of any age. The most recent wave of the UK tracking study carried out by MORI and the International Gaming Research Unit (IGRU) (2006) found that fruit machines were the most popular form of adolescent gambling with 54 per cent of their sample of 8,017 adolescent participants. The MORI/IGRU survey also found that:
- 17 per cent of adolescents are regular fruit machine players (playing at least once a week)
- 3.5 per cent of adolescents are probable pathological gamblers and/or have severe gambling-related difficulties.

All studies have reported that boys play on fruit machines more than girls and that as fruit machine playing becomes more regular it is more likely to be a predominantly male activity. Research has also indicated that very few female adolescents have gambling problems on fruit machines. Research suggests that irregular ('social') gamblers play for different reasons than the excessive ('pathological') gamblers. Social gamblers usually play for fun and entertainment (as a form of play), because their friends or parents do (ie it is a social activity), for the possibility of winning money, because it provides a challenge, because of ease of availability and there is little else to do, and/or for excitement (the 'buzz').

Pathological gamblers appear to play for other reasons such as mood modification and as a means of escape. As already highlighted, young males seem to be particularly susceptible to fruit machine addiction with a small but significant minority of adolescents in the UK experiencing problems with their fruit machine playing at any one time. Like other potentially addictive behaviours, fruit machine addiction causes the individual to engage in negative behaviours. This includes truanting in order to play the machines, stealing to fund machine playing, getting into trouble with teachers and/or parents over their machine playing, borrowing or the using of lunch money to play the machines, poor schoolwork, and in some cases aggressive behaviour (Griffiths, 2003b). These behaviours are not much different from those experienced by other types of adolescent problem gambling. In addition, fruit machine addicts also display bona fide signs of addiction including withdrawal effects, tolerance, mood modification, conflict and relapse.

It is clear that for some adolescents, gambling can cause many negative detrimental effects in their life. Education can be severely affected and they may acquire a criminal record as most problem gamblers have to resort to illegal behaviour to feed their addiction. Gambling is an adult activity and the government should consider legislation that restricts gambling to adults only.

Recommendations
- All adolescent gambling should be taken as seriously as adult problem gambling.
- There should be a review of slot machine gambling to assess whether it should be restricted to those over 18 years of age.
- Education and prevention programmes should be targeted at children and adolescents along with other potentially addictive and harmful behaviours (eg smoking, drinking, and drug taking).

Pathological features

Though many people engage in gambling as a form of recreation and enjoyment, or even as a means to gain an income, for some, gambling is associated with difficulties of varying severity and duration. Some regular gamblers persist in gambling even after repeated losses and develop significant, debilitating problems that typically result in harm to others close to them and in the wider community (Abbott & Volberg, 1999).

In 1980, pathological gambling was recognised as a mental disorder in the DSM-III under the section 'Disorders of Impulse Control' along with other illnesses such as kleptomania and pyromania (American Psychiatric Association, 1980). Adopting a medical model of pathological gambling in this way displaced the old image that the gambler was a sinner or a criminal. In diagnosing the pathological gambler, the DSM-III stated that the individual was chronically and progressively unable to resist impulses to gamble and that gambling compromised, disrupted or damaged family, personal, and vocational pursuits. The behaviour increased under times of stress and associated features included lying to obtain money, committing crimes (eg forgery, embezzlement or fraud), and concealment from others of the extent of the individual's gambling activities. In addition, the DSM-III stated that to be a pathological gambler, the gambling must not be due to antisocial personality disorder.

These criteria were criticised for (i) a middle class bias, ie the criminal offences like embezzlement and income tax evasion were 'middle class' offences, (ii) lack of recognition that many compulsive gamblers are self-employed and (iii) exclusion of individuals with antisocial personality disorder (Lesieur, 1988). Lesieur recommended the same custom be followed for pathological gamblers as for substance abusers and alcoholics in the past (ie allow for simultaneous diagnosis with no exclusions). The new criteria (DSM-III-R, American Psychiatric Association, 1987) were subsequently changed to take on board the criticisms and modelled extensively on substance abuse disorders due to the growing acceptance of gambling as a bona fide addictive behaviour. In 1989, however, Rosenthal conducted an analysis of the use of the DSM-III-R criteria by treatment professionals. It was reported that there was some dissatisfaction with the new criteria and that there was some preference for a compromise between the DSM-III and the DSM-III-R. As a consequence, the criteria were changed for DSM-IV.

The updated DSM-IV consists of 10 diagnostic criteria (see appendix 1). A 'problem gambler' is diagnosed when three or more of criteria A1-A10 are met, and a score of five or more indicates a 'probable pathological gambler.' The diagnosis is not made if the gambling behaviour is better accounted for by a manic episode (criterion B) (American Psychiatric Association, 1994). Problems with gambling may also occur in individuals with antisocial personality disorder and it is possible for an individual to be diagnosed with both pathological gambling and manic episode gambling behaviour if criteria for both disorders are met (American Psychiatric Association, 1994).

According to the American Psychiatric Association (1994) DSM-IV:
'Pathological gambling typically begins in early adolescence in males and later in life in females. Although a few individuals are "hooked" with their very first bet, for most the course is more insidious. There may be years of social gambling followed by an abrupt onset that may be precipitated by greater exposure to gambling or by a stressor. The gambling pattern may be regular or episodic, and the course of the disorder is typically chronic. There is generally a progression in the frequency of gambling, the amount wagered, and the preoccupation with gambling and obtaining money with which to gamble. The urge to gamble and gambling activity generally increase during periods of stress or depression.' (p617).

SOGS is based on the DSM-III criteria for pathological gambling and is at present the most widely used screening instrument for problem gambling internationally. It consists of 20 questions on gambling behaviour from which a total score (ranging from 0 to 20) of positive responses is calculated. A score of three to four indicates a 'problem gambler' and five or more indicates a 'probable pathological gambler' (see appendix 2).

Consequences and co-morbidities

Problem gambling is often co-morbid with other behavioural and psychological disorders, which can exacerbate, or be exacerbated by, problem gambling. Some of the psychological difficulties a problem gambler may experience include anxiety, depression, guilt, suicidal ideation and actual suicide attempts (Daghestani et al, 1996; Griffiths, 2004). Problem gamblers may also suffer irrational distortions in their thinking (eg denial, superstitions, overconfidence, or a sense of power or control) (Griffiths, 1994a). Increased rates of attention-deficit hyperactivity disorder (ADHD), substance abuse or dependence, antisocial, narcissistic, and borderline personality disorders have also been reported in pathological gamblers (American Psychiatric Association, 1994; Griffiths, 1994b). There is also some evidence that co-morbidities may differ among demographic subgroups and gambling types. For instance, young male slot machine gamblers are more likely to abuse solvents (Griffiths, 1994c).

There is frequently a link with alcohol or drugs as a way of coping with anxiety or depression caused by gambling problems, and, conversely, alcohol may trigger the desire to gamble (Griffiths, Parke & Wood, 2002). According to the DSM-IV, pathological gamblers tend to be highly competitive, energetic, restless, easily bored, and believe money is the cause of, and solution to, all their problems (see also Parke, Griffiths & Irwing, 2004). According to the American Psychiatric Association, pathological gamblers may also be overly concerned with the approval of others and may be extravagantly generous. Further, when not gambling, they may be workaholics or 'binge' workers who wait until they are up against deadlines before really working hard. Pathological gamblers may also be prone to stress-related physical illnesses including insomnia, hypertension, heart disease, stomach problems (eg peptic ulcer disease) and migraine (Daghestani et al, 1996; Abbot & Volberg, 2000; Griffiths, Scarfe & Bellringer, 2001; Griffiths, 2004). Like other addictive behaviours, while engaged in gambling, the body produces increased levels of endorphins (the body's own morphine-like substance), and other 'feel good' chemicals like noradrenaline and serotonin (Griffiths, 2006). Many of these negative physical effects may stem from the body's own neuro-adaptation processes.

Health-related problems due to problem gambling can also result from withdrawal effects. Rosenthal and Lesieur (1992) found that at least 65 per cent of problem gamblers reported at least one physical side-effect during withdrawal including insomnia, headaches, upset stomach, loss of appetite, physical weakness, heart racing, muscle aches, breathing difficulty and/or chills. Their results were also compared to the withdrawal effects from a substance-dependent control group. They concluded that problem gamblers experienced more physical withdrawal effects when attempting to stop than the substance-dependent group.

Interpersonal problems suffered by problem gamblers include conflict with family, friends and colleagues, and breakdown of relationships, often culminating in separation or divorce (Griffiths, 2004; 2006). The children of problem gamblers also suffer a range of problems, and tend to do less well at school (Jacobs, Marston, Singer et al, 1989; Lesieur & Rothschild, 1989). School- and work-related problems include poor work performance, abuse of leave time and job loss (Griffiths, 2002). Financial consequences include reliance on family and friends, substantial debt, unpaid creditors and bankruptcy (Griffiths, 2006). Finally, there may be legal problems as a result of criminal behaviour undertaken to obtain money to gamble or pay gambling debts (Griffiths, 2005b; 2006). The families of problem gamblers can also experience substantial physical and psychological difficulties (Griffiths & Delfabbo, 2001; Griffiths, 2006).

High levels of substance misuse and some other mental health disorders among problem gamblers highlight the importance of screening for gambling problems among participants in alcohol and drug treatment facilities, mental health centres and outpatient clinics, as well as probation services and prisons. Unfortunately, beyond programmes that provide specialised problem gambling services, few counselling professionals screen for gambling problems among their clients. Even when a gambling problem is identified, non-specialist professionals are often uncertain about the appropriate referrals to make or what treatments to recommend (Abbott et al, 2004). There is clearly a need for education and training in the diagnosis, appropriate referral and effective treatment of gambling problems.

Given the co-morbidity of alcoholism with gambling addiction, the recent introduction of 24-hour licensing may have an impact on the prevalence of gambling addiction. It is important that post-evaluative studies undertaken by the Department for Culture, Media and Sport (DCMS) to monitor the impact of the introduction of 24-hour licensing consider any potential impact this will have on levels of gambling addiction.

Recommendations
- Brief screening for gambling problems among participants in alcohol and drug treatment facilities, mental health centres and outpatient clinics, as well as probation services and prisons should be routine.
- The need for education and training in the diagnosis, appropriate referral and effective treatment of gambling problems must be addressed within GP training.
- Research into the effect 24-hour licensing laws have had on gambling problems as part of its post-evaluations and measurement of future effects must be conducted.

The importance of structural and situational characteristics

Gambling is a multifaceted rather than unitary phenomenon. Consequently, many factors may come into play in various ways and at different levels of analysis (eg biological, social or psychological). Theories may be complementary rather than mutually exclusive, which suggests that limitations of individual theories might be overcome through the combination of ideas from different perspectives. This has often been discussed in terms of recommendations for an 'eclectic' approach to gambling or a distinction between proximal and distal influences upon gambling (Walker, 1992). For the most part however, such discussions have been descriptive rather than analytical and, so far, few attempts have been made to explain why an adherence to a singular perspective is untenable. Put very simply, there are many different factors involved in how and why people develop gambling problems. Central to the latest thinking is that no single level of analysis is considered sufficient to explain either the aetiology or maintenance of gambling behaviour. Moreover, this view asserts that all research is context-bound and should be analysed from a combined, or biopsychosocial, perspective (Griffiths, 2005c). Variations in the motivations and characteristics of gamblers and in gambling activities themselves mean that findings obtained in one context are unlikely to be relevant or valid in another.

Another factor central to understanding gambling behaviour is the structure of gambling activities. Griffiths (1993; 1995; 1999) has shown that gambling activities vary considerably in their structural characteristics, such as the probability of winning, the amount of gambler involvement, the use of the near wins, the amount of skill that can be applied, the length of the interval between stake and outcome, and the magnitude of potential winnings. Structural variations are also observed within certain classes of activities such as slot machines, where differences in reinforcement frequency, colours, sound effects and machines' features can influence the profitability and attractiveness of machines significantly (Griffiths & Parke, 2003; Parke & Griffiths, 2006, in press). Each of these structural features may (and almost certainly does) have implications for gamblers' motivations and the potential 'addictiveness' of gambling activities.

For example, skilful activities that offer players the opportunity to use complex systems, study the odds and apply skill and concentration, appeal to many gamblers because their actions can influence the outcomes. Such characteristics attract people who enjoy a challenge when gambling. They may also contribute to excessive gambling if people overestimate the effectiveness of their gambling systems and strategies. Chantal and Vallerand (1996) have argued that people who gamble on these activities (eg racing punters) tend to be more intrinsically motivated than lottery gamblers in that they gamble for self-determination (ie to display their competence and to improve their performance).

People who gamble on chance activities, such as lotteries, usually do so for external reasons (ie to win money or escape from problems). This finding was confirmed by Loughnan, Pierce and Sagris (1997) in their clinical survey of problem gamblers. Here, racing punters emphasised the importance of skill and control considerably more than slot machine players. Although many slot machine players also overestimate the amount of skill involved in their gambling, other motivational factors (such as the desire to escape worries or to relax) tend to predominate. Thus, excessive gambling on slot machines may be more likely to result from people becoming conditioned to the tranquilising effect brought about by playing rather than just the pursuit of money.

Another vital structural characteristic of gambling is the continuity of the activity; namely, the length of the interval between stake and outcome. In nearly all studies, it has been found that continuous activities (eg racing, slot machines, casino games) with a more rapid play-rate are more likely to be associated with gambling problems (Griffiths, 1999). The ability to make repeated stakes in short time intervals increases the amount of money that can be lost and also increases the likelihood that gamblers will be unable to control spending. Such problems are rarely observed in non-continuous activities, such as weekly or bi-weekly lotteries, in which gambling is undertaken less frequently and where outcomes are often unknown for days. Consequently, it is important to recognise that the overall social and economic impact of expansion of the gambling industry will be considerably greater if the expanded activities are continuous rather than non-continuous.

Other factors central to understanding gambling behaviour are the situational characteristics of gambling activities. These are the factors that often facilitate and encourage people to gamble in the first place (Griffiths & Parke, 2003). Situational characteristics are primarily features of the environment (eg accessibility factors such as location of the gambling venue, the number of venues in a specified area and possible membership requirements) but can also include internal features of the venue itself (décor, heating, lighting, colour, background music, floor layout, refreshment facilities) or facilitating factors that may influence gambling in the first place (eg advertising, free travel and/or accommodation to the gambling venue, free bets or gambles on particular games) or influence continued gambling (eg the placing of a cash dispenser on the casino floor, free food and/or alcoholic drinks while gambling) (Griffiths & Parke, 2003; Abbott & Volberg, in press).

These variables may be important in both the initial decision to gamble and the maintenance of the behaviour. Although many of these situational characteristics are thought to influence vulnerable gamblers, there has been very little empirical research into these factors and more research is needed before any definitive conclusions can be made about the direct or indirect influence on gambling behaviour and whether vulnerable individuals are any more likely to be influenced by these particular types of marketing ploys. The introduction of super-casinos into the UK will almost certainly see an increase in these types of situational marketing strategies and should also provide an opportunity to research and monitor the potential psychosocial impact.

Support and treatment for problem gambling

'The majority of health and related professionals who have contact with problem gamblers are probably unaware that they do. Internationally, general population surveys indicate that the great majority of people identified as having problems with gambling do not report them to, or receive assistance from, professionals of any kind.' (Abbott et al, 2004, p11)

Gambling addiction treatment and services

The intervention options for the treatment of problem gambling include,[3] but are not limited to:

- counselling
- psychotherapy
- cognitive-behavioural therapy (CBT)
- advisory services
- residential care
- pharmacotherapy
- combinations of these (ie multi-modal treatment).

There is a very recent move towards surfing the internet as a route for guidance, counselling and treatment (Griiffiths & Cooper, 2003; Griffiths, 2005d). Treatment and support is provided from a range of different people (with and without formal medical qualifications), including specialist addiction nurses, counsellors, medics, psychologists, and psychiatrists. There are also websites and helplines to access information (eg *GamCare*) or discuss gambling problems anonymously (eg *GamAid*), and local support groups where problem gamblers can meet other people with similar experiences (eg *Gamblers Anonymous*). Support is also available for friends and family members of problem gamblers (eg *Gam Anon*).

Many private and charitable organisations throughout the UK provide support and advice for people with gambling problems. Some focus exclusively on the help, counselling and treatment of gambling addiction (eg *Gamblers Anonymous*, *GamCare*, *Gordon House Association*), while others also work to address common addictive behaviours such as alcohol and drug abuse (eg *Aquarius, Addiction Recovery Foundation, Connexions Direct, Priory*). The method and style of treatment varies between providers and can range from comprehensive holistic approaches to the treatment of gambling addiction (eg encouraging fitness, nutrition, alternative therapies and religious counselling), to an abstinence-based approach. Many providers also encourage patients (and sometimes friends and families) to join support groups (eg *Gamblers Anonymous* and *Gam Anon*), while others offer confidential one-to-one counselling and advice (eg *Connexions*). Most are non-profit making charities to which patients can self-refer and receive free treatment. Independent providers that offer residential treatment to gambling addicts are more likely to charge for their services. Some provide both inpatient treatment and day-patient services (eg *PROMIS*), and a decision as to the suitability of a particular intervention is made upon admission. For a list of private and charitable organisations that provide support and advice see appendix 3.

---

3   Griffiths, 1996; Griffiths & MacDonald, 1999; Griffiths & Delfabbro, 2001; Griffiths, Bellringer, Farrell-Roberts & Freestone, 2001; Hayer et al, 2005.

Due to the lack of relevant evaluative research, the efficacy of various forms of treatment intervention is almost impossible to address. Much of the documentation collected by treatment agencies is incomplete or collected in ways that make comparisons and assessments of efficacy difficult. As Abbott et al (2004) have noted, with such a weak knowledge base, little is known about which forms of treatment for problem gambling in the UK are most effective, how they might be improved or who might benefit from them. However, their review did note that individuals who seek help for gambling problems tend to be overwhelmingly male, aged between 18 to 45 years, and whose problems are primarily with on- and off-course betting, and slot machine use.

Recommendation
- Research into the efficacy of various approaches to the treatment of gambling addiction needs to be undertaken and should be funded by the Responsibility in Gambling Trust (RIGT).

Accessing treatment – referral paths

People suffering from problem gambling can access free or self-funded treatment via a number of routes.

Self-referrals: Problem gamblers can self-refer by contacting one of the many available community addiction centres and clinics where they can have an individual consultation before commencing a treatment programme. Some providers will allow individuals to drop in without an appointment. See appendix 3 for a list of organisations that can be contacted directly for help and advice.

GP referrals: Some GPs have undergone additional training in addiction management and run special clinics within their own surgery. When this is the case, a GP may not necessarily refer someone to another centre. Many GPs, however, will refer the person to the local addiction specialist for an assessment and a treatment plan. These units have specialist addiction management psychiatrists and nurses, counsellors, and social workers working with them. Often treatment is provided on a 'shared-care' basis. This may involve the GP providing certain parts of treatment, for example, appropriate prescriptions and treatment for addiction-related health problems, while the specialist addiction team provides ongoing monitoring and counselling. Where possible, a person is given the choice of where he or she is treated. Some prefer to be looked after in the familiar surroundings of their general practice, and even if the GP is not able to provide the treatment, arrangements can often be made for the person to be seen by the community specialist addiction nurse or counsellor within the general practice. Other people however, prefer to be looked after at a specialist addiction unit because of the anonymity this allows and the fact that everyone is there for the same reason (BBC Health: Help from your GP).

Private clinics: Some private clinics do not accept self-referrals. For example, Priory Hospital accepts potential patients for outpatient, day care and inpatient treatment only through referrals from GPs, an employee's company occupational health doctor (not a company occupational health nurse), or a non-Priory consultant (see www.prioryhealthcare.co.uk).

Court referrals: It is also worth mentioning that there are an increasing number of court cases involving problem gambling and that judges often give non-custodial sentences alongside referral for gambling treatment. One of the problems with this particular referral path is that the problem gambler may not have any motivation to stop. It is not unknown for a problem gambler to say they will attend gambling treatment as a way of helping them get a reduced sentence.

The gaming industry and gambling addiction services

The gaming industry has typically viewed pathological gambling as a rare mental disorder that is predominantly physically and/or psychologically determined. It supports recent findings that suggest many problem gamblers have transient problems that often self-correct. Currently, gambling providers in the UK are not compelled to supply patrons with help and advice about gambling problems, and have been reluctant to engage directly in interventions. Some gambling providers however, have taken the initiative to address the issue of gambling addiction within their businesses. Secondary prevention efforts by the gaming industry have included the development and implementation of employee training programmes, mandatory and voluntary exclusion programmes and gambling venue partnerships with practitioners and government agencies to provide information and improved access to formal treatment services (see appendix 3).

Implementation of secondary prevention efforts by the gaming industry, such as employee training programmes and exclusion programmes, have not always been of the highest quality and compliance has often been uneven. In addition, observations from abroad appear to demonstrate that efforts by the gaming industry to address gambling addiction tend to compete with heavily financed gaming industry advertising campaigns that may work directly to counteract their effectiveness (Griffiths, 2005e). Although advertising of gambling is very restricted at present, this is likely to become much more liberal over the next decade.

Problem gambling services and the NHS

Currently, there are almost no treatment services for problem gambling available on the NHS. Both the Budd Commission and the review commissioned by the RIGT (Abbott et al, 2004) recommended the adoption of a system of stepped care for the treatment of problem gambling. Such treatment could be integrated within existing NHS addiction services and be funded either through the RIGT or other gambling-derived revenue.

In this scenario, the modalities utilised for the treatment of drug problems could be adapted to suit the particular requirements of problem gamblers and to fit with the services and modalities that already exist in this area. It should also be noted however, that problem gambling is idiosyncratic and that analogies between problem gambling and other drug-based addictive disorders may not always be of direct relevance. Where possible, treatment should be based on individual needs following a full assessment.

Currently, almost all treatment for problem gambling is provided by private, charitable organisations, the major ones of which receive funding from the RIGT. The RIGT is an independent charitable body, funded by the UK gaming industry that commissions treatment, education and research into problem gambling. It was set up in response to recommendations made by the independent Gambling Review Body (the Budd Report),[4] which was commissioned by the government in 2001. The Budd Report recommended that an independent charitable trust should be set up and provided

---

4   This report, *Gambling Review Body Report* (DCMS, 2001), is commonly referred to as the Budd Report, as it was authored by the Gambling Review Body, the Chairman of which was Sir Alan Budd.

with voluntary funding by the gaming industry, to research and limit problem gambling. The trust decided to make progress in advance of the proposed new legislation, and by January 2005 it had paid annual grants in excess of £1m to organisations providing support for problem gamblers, and public education about the risks of gambling. *Gamcare* and *Gordon House* (organisations which help and treat problem gamblers) are two of the major recipients of funding from the RIGT.

The Budd Report recommended that the RIGT should be given around £3m per annum in funding and that if the industry did not fund the charitable trust, a statutory levy would be introduced. The current level of gaming industry donations is insufficient. Even if the industry donated £3m a year this equates to only £10 per adult problem gambler (based on there being 300,000 adult problem gamblers in the UK) – and that does not include help for adolescent problem gamblers. Three million pounds a year for all research, prevention, intervention, and treatment is inadequate and is 'small change' to a billion pound gaming industry.

Arrangements in which funding for *'problem gambling services comes largely through voluntary or mandatory levies on revenues derived from legalised gambling operations and generally flows through major academic institutions and/or quasi-governmental bodies'* is accepted practice internationally (Abbott et al, 2004, p15). It has been argued however, that problem gambling services in the UK should be provided under the NHS, as other addiction services are (Griffiths, 2001; 2004). Currently the *NHS Direct* website refers people inquiring about gambling addiction services to various private and charitable support organisations (including those listed in appendix 3). It is unclear whether the current system is preferable to one in which funding for problem gambling treatment services is provided through mandated levies from all sectors of the gaming industry, and/or a system in which treatment for problem gambling is funded directly by the government.

Recommendations
- Treatment for problem gambling should be provided under the NHS (either as stand alone services or alongside drug and alcohol addiction services) and funded either by the RIGT or other gambling-derived revenue.
- The gaming industry should pay at least £10 million per annum to fund research, prevention, intervention, and treatment programmes.

Impact of the Gambling Act 2005 on problem gambling

Although the BGPS found that Britain has a comparatively low rate of problem gambling (between 0.6% and 0.8% or 275,000 to 370,000 people; Sproston et al, 2000), this figure should be considered in the context of the (relatively) limited gambling opportunities available to the public at the time the survey was conducted in 1999. It has been predicted that the future expansion in gambling opportunities enabled by the Gambling Act 2005 (see appendix 4) can be expected to result in an increase in problem gambling in the UK (Griffiths, 2004). This is because the new legislation, due for full implementation in 2007, will significantly increase access to EGMs and other continuous gambling forms, including online gambling. Risk profiles are also likely to change, with disproportionate increases in problem gambling among women, ethnic and new migrant minorities. There is also concern about adolescent gambling, although the latest national prevalence survey did show that adolescent problem gambling is on the decrease (currently 3.5% in 2006, down from 4.9% in 2000) (MORI/IGRU, 2006). Newer technologies however, like internet gambling may be more attractive to this sub-group. While research is starting to suggest that increases in problems may level out over time (Abbott & Volberg, in press), this appears to be part of a complex process involving, among other things, social adaptation, the implementation of public health policies and the provision of specialist treatment services. It also appears to be an uneven process that affects different groups of people in different ways.

The Gambling Act 2005 enhances opportunities to gamble in a multitude of ways, and research has shown that increasing the availability of particular forms of gambling can have a significant impact on the prevalence of problem gambling within a community (Griffiths, 1999; 2003a). It is important to appreciate the differences between various forms of gambling and their link to problem gambling, as increasingly evidence suggests that some types of gambling are more strongly associated with gambling-related problems than others (see section on 'Profiling' above) (Abbott & Volberg, 1999).

Abbott (in press) has noted that in periods when new EGMs are being introduced or made highly accessible, substantial changes can occur over relatively short periods of time in the population sectors at highest risk for problem gambling. The RIGT notes that in that situation, existing services may need to change to be able to engage and work effectively with large numbers of different types of problem gambler. With disproportionate increases in problem gambling expected among women, youth, and ethnic and new migrant minorities, the development of targeted services and services that are culturally and demographically appropriate may be essential.

Abbott and Volberg (in press) have noted that raising public awareness of the risks of excessive gambling, expanding services for problem gamblers and strengthening regulatory, industry and public health harm reduction measures appear to counteract some adverse effects from increased availability. What is not known however, is how quickly such proactive mechanisms can have a significant impact and whether or not they can prevent problem gambling if they are introduced concurrently with increased access to 'harder' and more 'convenient' forms of gambling such as internet gambling (Griffiths, Parke, Wood & Parke, 2006).

Internet and remote gambling

The introduction of the internet and other remote gambling developments (such as mobile phone gambling and interactive television gambling) has the potential to lead to problematic gambling behaviour and is likely to be an issue over the next decade. Remote gambling presents what could be the biggest cultural shift in gambling and one of the biggest challenges concerning the psychosocial impact of gambling.

To date, there has been little empirical research examining remote gambling in the UK. The first prevalence survey was published in 2001 (from data collected in 1999) when internet gambling was almost non-existent (Griffiths, 2001). A recent report published by the DCMS (2006) however, noted that online gambling had more than doubled in the UK since 2001. Worldwide there are around 2,300 sites with a large number of these located in just a few particular countries. For instance, around 1,000 sites are based in Antigua and Costa Rica alone. The UK has about 70 betting and lottery sites but as yet no gaming sites (eg online casinos featuring poker, blackjack, roulette, etc.). The findings reported that there were approximately one million regular online gamblers in Britain alone making up nearly one-third of Europe's 3.3 million regular online gamblers. It was also reported that women were becoming increasingly important in the remote gambling market. For instance, during the 2006 World Cup, it was estimated that about 30 per cent of those visiting key UK based betting websites were women. The report also stated that Europe's regular online gamblers staked approximately £3.5bn pounds a year at around an average of £1,000 each. In addition, it was also predicted that mobile phone gambling was likely to grow, further increasing accessibility to remote gambling.

To date, knowledge and understanding of how the internet, mobile phones and interactive television affect gambling behaviour is sparse. Globally speaking, proliferation of internet access is still an emerging trend and it will take some time before the effects on gambling behaviour surface (on both adults and young people). However, there is strong foundation to speculate on the potential hazards of remote gambling. These include the use of virtual cash, unlimited accessibility, and the solitary nature of gambling on the internet as potential risk factors for problem gambling development (Griffiths & Parke, 2002; Griffiths, 2003c; 2005; Griffiths, Parke, Wood & Parke, 2006).

There is no conclusive evidence that internet gambling is associated with problem gambling, although very recent studies using self-selected samples suggest that the prevalence of problem gambling among internet gamblers is relatively high (Griffiths & Barnes, 2005; Wood, Griffiths & Parke, in press). What is clear, however, is that online gambling has strong potential to facilitate, or even encourage, problematic gambling behaviour (Griffiths, 2003c). Firstly, the 24-hour availability of internet gambling (and other remote forms) allows a person to potentially gamble non-stop (Griffiths, 1999). The privacy and anonymity offered by internet gambling enables problem gamblers to continue gambling without being 'checked' by gambling venue staff concerned about behaviour or amount of time spent gambling (Griffiths et al, 2005). Friends and family may also be oblivious to the amount of time an individual spends gambling online. In addition, the use of electronic cash may serve to distance a gambler from how much money he or she is spending, in a similar way that chips and tokens used in other gambling situations may allow a gambler to 'suspend judgement' with regard to money spent (Griffiths & Parke, 2002).

There are a number of factors that make online activities, such as internet gambling, potentially seductive and/or addictive including anonymity, convenience, escape, accessibility, event frequency, interactivity, short-term comfort, excitement and loss of inhibitions (Griffiths, 2003c; Griffiths et al, 2005). Further, there are many other specific developments that look likely to facilitate uptake of remote gambling services including (i) sophisticated gaming software, (ii) integrated e-cash systems (including multi-currency), (iii) multilingual sites, (iv) increased realism (eg 'real' gambling via webcams), (v) live remote wagering (for both gambling alone and gambling with others), and (vi) improving customer care systems (Griffiths, 2003c).

To a gambling addict, the internet could potentially be a very dangerous medium. For instance, it has been speculated that structural characteristics of the software itself might promote addictive tendencies. Structural characteristics promote interactivity and to some extent define alternative realities to the user and allow them feelings of anonymity – features that may be very psychologically rewarding to some individuals. There is no doubt that internet usage among the general population will continue to increase over the next few years. Despite evidence that both gambling and the internet can be potentially addictive, there is no evidence (to date) that internet gambling is 'doubly addictive', particularly as the internet appears to be just a medium to engage in the behaviour of choice. What the internet may do is facilitate social gamblers who use the internet (rather than internet users per se) to gamble more excessively than they would have done offline (Griffiths, 2003c; Griffiths et al, 2005). In addition, a recent survey of British internet gambling sites showed very low levels of social responsibility (Smeaton & Griffiths, 2004).

Technological advance in the form of remote gambling is providing 'convenience gambling'. Theoretically, people can gamble all day, every day of the year. This will have implications for the social impact of internet gambling. There are a number of social issues concerning internet gambling. Some of the major concerns are briefly described below and adapted from Griffiths and Parke (2002).

Gate-keeping and protection of the vulnerable: There are many groups of vulnerable individuals (eg young people, problem gamblers, drug/alcohol abusers and the learning impaired) who in offline gambling would be prevented from gambling by responsible members of the gaming industry. Remote gambling operators however, provide little in the way of 'gatekeeping'. In cyberspace, how can you be sure that young people do not have access to internet gambling by using a parent's credit card? How can you be sure that a person does not have access to internet gambling while they are under the influence of alcohol or other intoxicating substances? How can you prevent a problem gambler who may have been barred from one internet gambling site, simply clicking to the next internet gambling link?

Electronic cash: For most gamblers, it is very likely that the psychological value of electronic cash (e-cash) will be less than 'real' cash (and similar to the use of chips or tokens in other gambling situations). Gambling with e-cash may lead to a 'suspension of judgment'. The 'suspension of judgment' refers to a structural characteristic that temporarily disrupts the gambler's financial value system and potentially stimulates further gambling. This is well known by both those in commerce (ie people typically spend more on credit and debit cards because it is easier to spend money using plastic) and by the gaming industry. This is the reason that 'chips' are used in casinos and why tokens are used on some slot machines. In essence, chips and tokens 'disguise' the money's true value (ie decrease the psychological value of the money to be gambled). Tokens and chips are often re-gambled without hesitation as the psychological value is much less than the real value.

Increased odds of winning in practice modes: One of the most common ways that gamblers can be facilitated to gamble online is when they try out games in the 'demo', 'practice' or 'free play' mode. Further, there are no restrictions preventing children and young people playing (and learning how to gamble) on these practice and demonstration modes. Recent research (Sevigny et al, 2005) showed that it was significantly more commonplace to win while 'gambling' on the first few goes on a 'demo' or 'free play' game. They also reported that it was commonplace for gamblers to have extended winning streaks during prolonged periods while playing in the 'demo' modes. Obviously, once gamblers start to play for real with real money, the odds of winning are considerably reduced. This has some serious implications for young people's potential gambling behaviour.

Online customer tracking: Perhaps the most worrying concern over remote gambling is the way operators can collect other sorts of data about the gambler. Remote gamblers can provide tracking data that can be used to compile customer profiles. When signing up for remote gambling services, players supply lots of information including name, address, telephone number, date of birth, and gender. Remote gambling service providers will know a player's favourite game and the amounts that they have wagered. Basically they can track the playing patterns of any gambler. They will know more about the gambler's playing behaviour than the gamblers themselves. They will be able to send the gambler offers and redemption vouchers, complimentary accounts, etc. The industry claims all of these things are introduced to enhance customer experience. More unscrupulous operators however, will be able to entice known problem gamblers back on to their premises with tailored freebies (such as the inducement of 'free' bets in the case of remote gambling).

Given the brief outline above, remote gambling could easily become a medium for problematic gambling behaviour. Even if numbers of problem remote gamblers are small (and they by no means necessarily are), remote gambling remains a matter of concern. Remote gambling is a relatively new phenomenon and is likely to continue expanding in the near future. It is therefore crucial that the new legislation does nothing to facilitate the creation or escalation of problems in relation to remote gambling. The recent decision in the USA to ban internet gambling by making it illegal to pay with debit and credit cards is likely to drive the problem of internet gambling 'underground' and result in even less protection for vulnerable gamblers. New innovative ways of paying electronically for internet gambling will emerge and the prohibitive stance taken by the USA is likely to have little long-lasting protective effect.

Recommendation
- Research into the association of internet gambling and problem gambling should be conducted.

Recommendations

Healthcare professionals:

- **should be aware of the types of gambling and problem gambling, demographic and cultural differences, and the problems and common co-morbidities associated with problem gambling.**

- **should receive education and training, within GP training, in the diagnosis, appropriate referral and effective treatment of gambling problems.**

- **should understand the importance of screening patients perceived to be at increased risk of gambling addiction.** They should be aware of the referral and support services available locally.

Gambling operators and service providers:

- **should supply information on gambling addiction, treatment and services to patrons.**

- **should support development of centralised training for gambling venue staff to ensure uniform standards and accreditation.**

- **should pay at least £10m per annum to fund research, prevention, intervention, and treatment programmes.** In Britain, the Budd Commission mandated a £3m per annum levy on the industry to pay for problem gambling research, education and treatment. This fund is administered by the RIGT.

Services

- **Information about gambling addiction services, in particular services in the local area, should be readily available to gamblers.** Although some gambling services (such as *GamCare* and *GamAid*) provide information to problem gamblers about local services, such information is provided to problem gamblers who have already been proactive in seeking gambling help and/or information.

- **Treatment for problem gambling should be provided under the NHS (either as stand alone services or alongside drug and alcohol addiction services) and funded either by the RIGT or other gambling-derived revenue.** Such provision could follow the tiered system of treatment used for drug addiction, as outlined in the DH Models of Care (2002) document. Both the Budd Commission and the review commissioned by the Responsibility in Gambling Trust (Abbott et al, 2004) recommended the adoption of a system of stepped care for the treatment of problem gambling.

- **Provision of nationally dedicated problem gambling treatment, advice and counselling services both in and outside of the NHS should be expanded.** At present, such provision is sparse and unevenly distributed throughout the country. Wherever possible, information and treatment services should be sited close to gambling venues, as research suggests that increased proximity of the former to the latter increases the efficacy of support.

- **Funding should be sought from the DH for the development and evaluation of targeted services (such as for ethnic minorities, young people, women, and family members).**

Screening

- **Brief screening for gambling problems among participants in alcohol and drug treatment facilities, mental health centres and outpatient clinics, as well as probation services and prisons should be routine.**

Information and education

- **Funding should be sought from both the DH and Department for Education and Skills (DfES) for public health education about the risks of gambling.** Given that severe problem gambling is difficult to treat, and that large numbers of the population may be at risk from developing problems with their behaviour, it makes sense to focus on public health and awareness raising initiatives in order to prevent the development of problems in the first place.

Youth gambling

- **All adolescent gambling should be taken as seriously as adult problem gambling.**

- **There should be a review of slot machine gambling to assess whether it should be restricted to those over 18 years of age.**

- **Education and prevention programmes should be targeted at children and adolescents along with other potentially addictive and harmful behaviours (eg smoking, drinking, and drug taking).**

Research

Understanding problem gambling is seriously hindered by a lack of high quality data, both internationally and especially in Britain. It is important to expand the research base on the causes, progression, distribution and treatment of gambling problems. One way to begin tackling the problem could be to link up with overseas networks and researchers in order to pool knowledge and expertise. The RIGT should also provide funding for major research programmes. Gambling as a health issue could also be included in other national surveys on health (such as the General Health Survey).

There should be:

- **regular surveys of problem gambling services, including help lines and formal treatment providers, and evaluations of the effectiveness and efficacy of these services.**

- **research undertaken into the efficacy of various approaches to the treatment of gambling addiction and this should be funded by the RIGT.**

- **research conducted into the association of internet gambling and problem gambling.**

- **research into the impacts of gambling, including health, family, workplace, financial and legal impacts.**

- **research into the effect 24-hour licensing laws have had on gambling problems as part of its post-evaluations and measurement of future effects.**

- **long-term studies conducted into problem gambling, treatment, and the impact of gambling legislation on prevalence of problem gambling. In particular, why some people develop problems and, just as importantly, why the majority do not develop problems.**

Glossary

Aetiology is the study of the cause of a disorder/disease

Antisocial personality disorder is a disorder characterised by an ongoing disregard for other's rights

Attention deficit hyperactivity disorder (ADHD) is a behavioural disorder characterised by inattention, impulsivity and hyperactivity

Borderline personality disorder is a disorder characterised by a pattern of instability in relationships and by impulsivity

Cognitive-behavioural therapy (CBT) is a form of therapy that addresses both thinking patterns and behaviour

Co-morbidity is where one or more disorders/diseases co-exist with a primary disorder/disease

Endorphins are neurotransmitters produced in the brain that have pain-relieving properties similar to morphine

Fixed odds betting terminals are electronic gaming machines with fixed odds for each event, and limited stake and prize amounts

Hypertension is the condition of high blood pressure

Kleptomania is a disorder characterised by a compulsion to steal

Manic episode describes a period of abnormal high energy

Narcissistic personality disorder is a disorder characterised by an inflated sense of self-importance

Noradrenaline is a hormone produced by the adrenal gland, which increases the concentration of glucose in the blood, raises blood pressure and heartbeat rate, and increases muscular power and resistance to fatigue. It is also one of the principal neurotransmitters

Pathological gambling is a disorder characterised by persistent and recurrent maladaptive gambling behaviour

Pharmacotherapy is the practice of treating diseases with medication

Pyromania is a disorder characterised by an obsession with fire and starting fires

Serotonin is a neurotransmitter with a diverse range of actions including the control of appetite, sleep, memory and learning, temperature regulation, mood, behaviour, cardiovascular function, muscle contraction, endocrine regulation and depression

Further information

This listing of organisations and publications is intended for further information only. The BMA is not responsible for the content or accuracy of external websites, nor does it endorse or otherwise guarantee the veracity of statements made in non-BMA publications.

Birmingham Alcohol, Drugs, Gambling and Addiction Research (BADGAR)

http://psg275.bham.ac.uk/research_03/adar.htm

This is a collaborative group that carries out research into the consumption of alcohol, drugs and gambling activity, both in the case of unexceptional behaviour and excessive behaviour or addiction.

Centre for the Study of Gambling

www.gamblingstudies.salford.ac.uk

The aim of the centre is to undertake research into the gambling industry, to teach those interested in a career in the gambling industry and to increase public understanding.

Department for Culture Media and Sport (DCMS)

www.culture.gov.uk

The DCMS is responsible for the legal regulation of gambling and racing, and sponsors these industries. The department works closely with the Gambling Commission, and is currently implementing the Gambling Act 2005. For the text of the Gambling Act 2005, and explanatory notes, please visit Her Majesty's Stationery Office (HMSO) website at www.opsi.gov.uk

European Association for the Study of Gambling (EASG)

www.easg.org

The association provides a forum for sharing knowledge relating to gambling in Europe. EASG provides information on Gambling and organises conferences.

Gambling Commission

www.gamblingcommission.gov.uk

This is a non-departmental public body that works closely with the DCMS and RIGT. The Gambling Commission will regulate all commercial gambling in Great Britain, under the Gambling Act 2005. Its primary aims are to keep crime out of gambling, to protect vulnerable people and to ensure that gambling is undertaken fairly and openly.

Global Remote and E-Gambling Research Institute (GREGRI)

www.gregri.org

The GREGRI is a research organisation that conducts research into a wide range of aspects of remote gambling and e-gambling.

Institute for Problem Gambling

www.gamblingproblem.net

The Institute provides education and training on problem gambling, with the aim of reducing its impact on individuals, families, businesses and society.

Institute for Research on Pathological Gambling and Related Disorders

www.divisiononaddictions.org/institute

The Institute is a programme of Harvard Medical School's Addictions Division, and is supported by the US National Centre for Responsible Gaming. The Institute funds scientific research on pathological gambling and related psychiatric disorders.

International Gaming Research Unit (IGRU)

http://ess.ntu.ac.uk/gamingresearch

The IGRU conducts research into attitudes and behaviour relating to gaming, risk taking and interactive technologies.

National Centre for Responsible Gaming (US)

www.ncrg.org

The centre funds scientific research into pathological and youth gambling, with the hope of finding methods for both prevention and treatment of the problem.

National Lottery Commission

www.natlotcomm.gov.uk

The National Lottery Commission is responsible for licensing and regulating the National Lottery.

Responsible Gambling Council (Canada)

www.responsiblegambling.org

The Council is an independent organisation working towards preventing problem gambling, through research, information and awareness campaigns.

Responsibility in Gambling Trust (RIGT)

www.rigt.org.uk

The RIGT is an independent trust funded by the gambling industry. The aim of the trust is to reduce the likelihood of people becoming problem gamblers, and to increase the likelihood that problem gamblers will seek and have access to effective help. The Trust raises awareness of problem gambling, and commissions treatment, education and research into problem gambling.

Society for the Study of Gambling

www.societystudygambling.co.uk

The Society provides a forum for those concerned in gambling research. It produces a newsletter and holds bi-annual meetings on current topics in gambling.

Trade Associations:

- The Association of British Bookmakers: www.abb.uk.com
- The Bingo Association: www.bingo-association.co.uk
- The British Casino Association: www.britishcasinoassociation.org.uk
- The British Amusement Catering Trade Association: www.bacta.org.uk
- The Remote Gambling Association: www.rga.eu.com
- The World Lottery Association: www.world-lotteries.org

Appendix 1

DSM-IV Diagnostic criteria for pathological gambling

The updated DSM-IV consists of 10 diagnostic criteria. A 'problem gambler' is diagnosed when three or more of criteria A1-A10 are met, and a score of five or more indicates a 'probable pathological gambler'. The diagnosis is not made if the gambling behaviour is better accounted for by a manic episode.

A. Persistent and recurrent maladaptive gambling behaviour as indicated by five (or more) of the following:
(1)   is preoccupied with gambling (eg preoccupied with reliving past gambling experiences, handicapping or planning next venture, or thinking of ways to get money with which to gamble)
(2)   needs to gamble with increasing amounts of money in order to achieve the desired excitement
(3)   has repeated unsuccessful efforts to control, cut back, or stop gambling
(4)   is restless or irritable when trying to cut down or stop gambling
(5)   gambles as a way of escaping from problems or of relieving a dysphoric mood (eg feelings of helplessness, guilt, anxiety, depression)
(6)   after losing money gambling, often returns another day to get even ('chasing' one's losses)
(7)   lies to family members, therapist, or others to conceal extent of involvement with gambling
(8)   has committed illegal acts such as forgery, fraud, theft, or embezzlement to finance gambling
(9)   has jeopardised or lost a significant relationship, job, or educational or career opportunity because of gambling
(10)   relies on others to provide money to relieve a desperate financial situation caused by gambling.

B. The gambling behaviour is not better accounted for by a manic episode.

Source: American Psychiatric Association (1994) *Diagnostic and Statistical Manual of Mental Disorders*, fourth edition (DSM-IV), pp615-6.

Appendix 2

South Oaks Gambling Screen (SOGS)

SOGS is based on the DSM-III criteria for pathological gambling and is at present the most widely used screen instrument for problem gambling internationally. It consists of 20 questions on gambling behaviour from which a total score (ranging from 0 to 20) of positive responses is calculated. A score of three to four indicates a 'problem gambler' and five or more indicates a 'probable pathological gambler'.

1. Please indicate which of the following types of gambling you have done in your lifetime. For each type, mark one answer: 'not at all', 'less than once a week', or 'once a week or more'.

Not at all	Less than once a week	Once a week or more	
☐	☐	☐	a. played cards for money
☐	☐	☐	b. bet on horses, dogs or other animals (in off-track betting, at the track or with a bookie)
☐	☐	☐	c. bet on sports (parley cards, with a bookie, or at jai alai)
☐	☐	☐	d. played dice games (including craps, over and under, or other dice games) for money
☐	☐	☐	e. went to casino (legal or otherwise)
☐	☐	☐	f. played the numbers or bet on lotteries
☐	☐	☐	g. played bingo
☐	☐	☐	h. played the stock and/or commodities market
☐	☐	☐	i. played slot machines, poker machines or other gambling machines
☐	☐	☐	j. bowled, shot pool, played golf or played some other game of skills for money

2. What is the largest amount of money you have ever gambled within any one day?
    ☐ never have gambled
    ☐ $10 or less
    ☐ more than $10 up to $100
    ☐ more than $100 up to $1,000
    ☐ more than $1,000 up to $10,000
    ☐ more than $10,000

3. Do (did) your parents have a gambling problem?
    ☐ both my father and mother gamble (or gambled) too much
    ☐ my father gambles (or gambled) too much
    ☐ my mother gambles (or gambled) too much
    ☐ neither gambles (or gambled) too much

4. When you gamble, how often do you go back another day to win back money you lost?
    ☐ never
    ☐ some of the time (less than half the time) I lost
    ☐ most of the time I lost
    ☐ every time I lost

5. Have you ever claimed to be winning money gambling but weren't really? In fact, you lost?
    ☐ never (or never gamble)
    ☐ yes, less than half the time I lost
    ☐ yes, most of the time

6. Do you feel you have ever had a problem with gambling?
    ☐ no
    ☐ yes, in the past, but not now
    ☐ yes

		Yes	No
7.	Did you ever gamble more than you intended?	☐	☐
8.	Have people criticized your gambling?	☐	☐
9.	Have you ever felt guilty about the way you gamble or what happens when you gamble?	☐	☐
10.	Have you ever felt like you would like to stop gambling but didn't think you could?	☐	☐
11.	Have you ever hidden betting slips, lottery tickets, gambling money, or other signs of gambling from your spouse, children, or other important people in you life?	☐	☐
12.	Have you ever argued with people you like over how you handle money?	☐	☐
13.	(If you answered 'yes' to question 12): Have money arguments ever centered on your gambling?	☐	☐
14.	Have you ever borrowed from someone and not paid them back as a result of your gambling?	☐	☐
15.	Have you ever lost time from work (or school) due to gambling?	☐	☐
16.	If you borrowed money to gamble or to pay gambling debts, where did you borrow from? (Check 'yes' or 'no' for each)		
	a. from household money	☐	☐
	b. from your spouse	☐	☐
	c. from other relatives or in-laws	☐	☐
	d. from banks, loan companies or credit unions	☐	☐
	e. from credit cards	☐	☐
	f. from loan sharks (Shylocks)	☐	☐
	g. your cashed in stocks, bonds or other securities	☐	☐
	h. you sold personal or family property	☐	☐
	i. you borrowed on your checking account (passed bad checks)	☐	☐
	j. you have (had) a credit line with a bookie	☐	☐
	k. you have (had) a credit line with a casino	☐	☐

Scores are determined by adding up the number of questions that show an 'at risk' response, indicated as follows. If you answer the questions above with one of the following answers, mark the space next to that question:

Questions 1-3 are not counted.

☐ Question 4: most of the time I lost, or every time I lost
☐ Question 5: yes, less than half the time I lose, or yes, most of the time
☐ Question 6: yes, in the past, but not now, or yes
☐ Question 7: yes
☐ Question 8: yes
☐ Question 9: yes
☐ Question 10: yes
☐ Question 11: yes

Question 12 is not counted

☐ Question 13: yes
☐ Question 14: yes
☐ Question 15: yes
☐ Question 16a: yes
☐ Question 16b: yes
☐ Question 16c: yes
☐ Question 16d: yes
☐ Question 16e: yes
☐ Question 16f: yes
☐ Question 16g: yes
☐ Question 16h: yes
☐ Question 16i: yes

Questions 16j and 16k are not counted

Total = ☐ (20 questions are counted)**

**3 or 4 = potential pathological gambler (problem gambler)
**5 or more = probable pathological gambler

Appendix 3

Treatment, support and advice for people with gambling addiction

Many private and charitable organisations throughout the UK provide support and advice for people with gambling problems.

Aquarius: works with GamCare to deliver interventions for people with gambling problems. Its counsellors receive training from GamCare.
Aquarius Action Projects
2nd Floor
16 Kent Street
Birmingham
B5 6RD
Tel: 0121 622 8181
Fax: 0121 622 8189
Email: whitehouse@aquarius.org.uk
Website: www.aquarius.org.uk

Addiction Recovery Foundation: free self-referral service. Helpline provides advice, support and guidance to those experiencing gambling addiction and other problems. Provides details of self-help groups. The foundation also promotes and assists in the teaching or training of anyone engaged in the care or treatment of people with addiction or dependency problems.
Addiction Recovery Foundation
193 Victoria Street
London
W1E 5NE
Tel: 020 7233 5333
Fax: 020 7233 8123
Website: www.addictiontoday.co.uk

Connexions Direct: free self-referral service for 13 to 19 year olds, parents, carers and advocates for young people. Confidential helpline is available via telephone, email, SMS text, webchat and minicom. Connexions services are available for face-to-face contact with a personal adviser at a local Connexions Centre.
Phone and callback: 080 800 13219
Adviser online: www.cxdirect.com/Visitor/IndexTalk.htm
Text: 07766413219
Textphone: 08000 968 336
Website: www.connexions-direct.com

GamCare: a registered charity that provides information, counselling and advice, education and training resources, publications and research on addressing the social impact of gambling.
GamCare
2&3 Baden Place
Crosby Row
London
SE1 1YW
Tel: 020 7378 5200
Fax: 020 7378 5233
Helpline: 0845 6000 133 (24 hour, 7 days a week)
Email: info@gamcare.org.uk
Contact an individual member of staff: http://www.gamcare.org.uk/about.php
Website: www.gamcare.org.uk

Gamblers Anonymous: provides information, support and advice for problem gamblers, their partners, families and friends. There are numerous national 'chapters' (ie self-help groups) that meet up at least weekly.
Helplines:
National and London 020 7384 3040
Sheffield 0114 262 0026
Manchester 0161 976 5000
Birmingham 0121 233 1335
Glasgow 08700 50 88 81
Londonderry 028 7135 1329.
Website: www.gamblersanonymous.org.uk

Gam-Anon UK & Ireland: allied to Gamblers Anonymous, it provides support and advice for the friends and families of problem gamblers. There are also self-help support groups nationally.
Gam-Anon
National Service Office
PO Box 88
London
SW10 0EU
National Helpline 08700 50 88 80
London 020 7384 3040
Midlands 0121 233 1335
North East 0114 262 0026
North West 0161 976 5000
Scotland 0141 630 1033
Email: contact@gamanon.org.uk
Website: www.gamanon.org.uk

Gordon House Association: provides an Outreach Support Service and set up an internet counselling service (*GamAid*) which has now branched out separately. It is the only specialist provider of residential treatment to severely addicted gamblers in the UK. Gordon House Association accepts individuals who have been referred by anyone (including themselves, friends, family, probation, social or health workers) as long as the person being referred agrees. There is no charge to those in treatment services provided the individual is eligible for state benefits.
GHA Branches:
Gordon House Central Office
114 Wellington Road
Dudley
West Midlands
DY1 1UB
Gordon House in the Midlands
Tel: 01384 241292
Fax: 01384 251959
Gordon House in the South East
Tel: 020 8778 3331
Fax: 020 8659 5036
Email: help@gordonhouse.org.uk
Website: www.gordonhouse.org.uk

The Life Works Compulsive Gambling Programme: offers an individual-specific treatment plan for clients with a gambling problem. The Life Works Treatment Programme is an abstinence based 12-step programme. A variety of therapeutic models are used and delivered in proven methods from group, one to one, psycho-education and experiential therapy. All programmes are underpinned by a strong Family Programme and a thorough aftercare plan while integrating a holistic approach including nutrition, exercise, alternative therapies and spiritual counselling. For general inquiries regarding individual-specific programmes, costs and length of treatment, call freephone number 0800 081 0700.
Life Works Community Ltd
The Grange
High Street
Old Woking
Surrey
GU22 8LB
Tel: 01483 757 572
Fax: 01483 755 966
Life Works Duke Street
No 4 Duke Street
London
W1U 3EL
Tel: 020 7486 7177
Fax: 020 7487 2798
Email: enquiries@lifeworkscommunity.com
Website: www.lifeworkscommunity.com/programmes/gambling_addiction.asp

The Living Room: a day-care rehabilitation centre. An independent non-profit making charity offering a range of free addiction treatment services including a non-residential structured treatment programme and structured one-to-one counselling, and support for family and friends. Clients are referred by their family doctor or another health or social care professional. Patients can 'self refer' by calling 01438 355649. For professionals working in health or social care a full service description is available in PDF format.
The Living Room
8-10 The Glebe
Chells Way
Stevenage
SG2 0DJ
Website: www.thelivingroom.me.uk

PROMIS: accepts referrals from any source. Following an assessment, patients may be admitted to the Recovery Centre in Kent for inpatient treatment, or to the Counselling Centre in London for day-patient services.
The PROMIS Recovery Centre
The Old Court House
Pinners Hill
Nonington
Kent
CT15 4LL
Tel: 01304 841700
Fax: 01304 841917
Email: enquiries@promis.co.uk
The PROMIS Counselling Centre
10 Kendrick Mews
South Kensington
London
SW7 3HG
Tel: 020 7581 8222
Fax: 020 7581 8515
Email: enquiries@promis.co.uk
Website: www.promis.co.uk
24/7 Confidential Enquiries & Advice Line: 0800 374 318

Priory: provides residential treatment for sufferers of alcoholism, drug addiction, gambling and eating disorders. Accommodation located in Surrey. The staff consists of consultant psychiatrist doctors, nurses, counsellors, clergyman and sessional therapists for fitness training/yoga/dietary matters. Patient and family members are encouraged to be involved in aftercare counselling, support groups and reunions. An aftercare plan is organised with each patient before they leave treatment. The length of treatment varies with the individual and comprises of a 12 to 24 week residential stay. GP, corporate and consultant referrals only.

Farm Place
Stane Street
Ockley
Nr Dorking
Surrey
RH5 5NG
Tel: 01306 627742
Fax: 01306 627756
Email: farmplace@prioryhealthcare.com
Website: www.prioryhealthcare.co.uk/Find-a-centre/Facilities/Farm-Place

RCA Trust: a GamCare affiliate, and the only organisation in Scotland to provide services for problem gamblers.

RCA Trust
Mirren House
Back Sneddon Street
Paisley
PA3 2AF
Tel: 0141 887 0880
Fax: 0141 887 8063
Helpline: 0845 230 0038
Website: www.rcatrust.org.uk

Appendix 4

The Gambling Act 2005

Legalisation of gambling in the UK has largely been a 20th century development. Bingo was brought to Britain by troops returning from the Second World War and, with the Betting and Gaming Act 1960, bingo halls were set up throughout the country. The legalisation of casinos under the 1960 Act limited the number of gaming machines in each venue to 10, although the difficulty in enforcing this led to further liberalisation under the Gaming Act 1968. The 1960 Act also legalised off-course bookmakers for betting on competitive sports events. A 1934 Act legalised small lotteries, which was further liberalised in 1956 and 1976. In 1994, the UK's largest lottery – the National Lottery – was introduced under government licence. Several games are now run under this brand, including Lotto, Euro Millions, and Thunderball.

Currently, gambling in Britain is regulated by the Gambling Commission on behalf of the DCMS under the Gambling Act 2005. This Act of Parliament significantly updated gambling laws, including the introduction of a new structure of protections for children and vulnerable adults, as well as bringing the burgeoning internet gambling sector within British regulation for the first time. The Gambling Act 2005 extends to the whole of Great Britain. Separate arrangements have been developed for Northern Ireland. The DCMS is working with the Gambling Commission, local authorities, problem gambling charities and the industry to oversee the implementation of the Act. The target for full implementation is 1 September 2007. The new system is based on tri-partite regulation by the new Gambling Commission, licensing authorities and by the government:

Gambling Commission
The Gambling Commission, which replaced The Gaming Board for Great Britain, is the new, independent, national regulator for commercial gambling in Great Britain. It will issue operating licences to providers of gambling and personal licences to certain personnel in those operations. Its remit will encompass most of the main forms of commercial gambling, including casinos, bingo, betting, gaming machines, pool betting and the larger charity lotteries. It will license providers that operate premises and those that offer gambling through 'remote' technologies, like the internet and mobile telephones. The commission may impose conditions on licences and issue codes of practice about how those conditions can be achieved. Where licence conditions are breached, various administrative and criminal sanctions can be applied.

Licensing authorities
Licensing authorities (in England and Wales, local authorities, and in Scotland, Licensing Boards) will license gambling premises and issue a range of permits to authorise other gambling facilities in their locality. Authorities will be independent of government and the Gambling Commission, but in the exercise of their functions they must have regard to guidance issued by the commission. Authorities will have similar regulatory powers to the commission with respect to their licensees, including powers to impose conditions, but they will not be able to impose financial penalties. The number of casinos, racecourses, bookmakers and bingo halls requiring a gaming licence will be approximately 30,000.

The government

The government has responsibility for setting various rules on how gambling is conducted. For example, it will make regulations defining categories of gaming machine. Powers are also available for the government to set licence conditions on operating and personal licences, and for the government, in England and Wales, and the Scottish Executive, in Scotland, to set conditions on premises' licences. In some cases licensing authorities will be able to alter these central conditions. The government also wishes to see a sustainable programme of research into the causes of problem gambling and into effective methods of counselling and treatment intervention. The government has actively supported the creation of an industry-funded Responsibility in Gambling Trust to take forward these and other programmes.

An important aspect of the government's policy is the power of the Gambling Commission to intervene in the operation of gambling across the entire industry so that it can address factors that evidence suggests are related to risks of problem gambling. In this context, the government proposes new safeguards for gaming machines. These will be enforced through statutory instruments, licence conditions and codes of practice. They may include the powers:
- to control speed of play
- to control game design features such as 'near misses' and progressive tiers, which may reinforce incentives to repeat play
- to require information about odds and actual wins or losses in the play session to be displayed on screen
- to require 'reality checks' or the need to confirm continuing play
- to implement loss limits set by players before starting through use of smart card technology
- to vary stake and prize limits.

Casinos

At present there are 140 casinos, 969 bingo halls, 8,800 betting offices, 1,760 arcades, 19,000 private members clubs and 60 racecourses throughout the UK. An important element of the introduction of the Gambling Act 2005 is the licensing of 17 new casinos in addition to those already in existence. Licences for eight large casinos, eight smaller casinos and a super-casino are currently being offered. The new super-casino will have a 5,000 square metre gaming area largely filled with 1,250 unlimited-jackpot slot machines. Currently seven locations are competing for licensing permission to build the super-casino, including Glasgow, Cardiff, Greenwich and Blackpool. The 16 smaller venues will offer fewer slot machines with much lower jackpots, but will probably support more poker games. Bath, Bournemouth, Cornwall and Hull are among 60 local authorities to have applied for a regional casino licence.

Online gambling

The regulation of online gambling is fraught with problems. Preventing under-age gambling is difficult, if not impossible, as there is no way of determining whether an adolescent or child is using a parents' credit or debit card to gamble online. Likewise, it is impossible to tell whether a person is gambling while under the influence of alcohol or other drugs, or is suffering from a gambling addiction. The 24-hour availability of online gambling is problematic for those with, or at risk of developing, gambling problems, as there is currently nothing stopping a person from gambling 24-hours a day (Griffiths & Parke, 2002; Griffiths, 2003c).

References

Abbott MW (in press) Do EGMs and problem gambling go together like a horse and carriage? *Gambling Research*.

Abbott MW & Volberg RA (1999) *Gambling and problem gambling in the community: an international overview and critique. Report number one of the New Zealand Gaming Survey.* Wellington: Department of Internal Affairs.

Abbott, MW & Volberg RA (2000) *Taking the pulse on gambling and problem gambling in New Zealand: Phase One of the 1999 National Prevalence Survey. Report number three of the New Zealand Gaming Survey.* Wellington: Department of Internal Affairs.

Abbott M, Volberg R & Bellringer M et al (2004) *A review of research on aspects of problem gambling*. Auckland University of Technology, Gambling Research Centre. London: Responsibility in Gambling Trust.

Abbott M & Volberg R (in press) Situational factors that affect gambling behaviour. In: Smith G, Hodgins D & Williams R (eds) *Research and measurement issues in gambling studies*. New York: Elsevier.

American Psychiatric Association (1980) *Diagnostic and statistical manual of mental disorders (third edition)*. Washington, DC.

American Psychiatric Association (1987) *Diagnostic and statistical manual of mental disorders (third edition - revised)*. Washington, DC.

American Psychiatric Association (1994) *Diagnostic and statistical manual of mental disorders (fourth edition)*. Washington, DC.

BBC Health (2001) *Help from your GP* (www.bbc.co.uk/health/conditions/addictions/treatmentaddiction_gp.shtml, accessed Nov 2006).

Chantal Y & Vallerand RJ (1996) Skill versus luck: a motivational analysis of gambling involvement. *Journal of Gambling Studies* **12**: 407-18.

Creigh-Tyte S & Lepper J (2004) *Technical Paper No. 4: Gender difference in participation, and attitudes towards, gambling in the UK: Results from the 2004 NOP Survey*. London: DCMS.

Daghestani AN, Elenz E & Crayton JW (1996) Pathological gambling in hospitalised substance abusing veterans. *Journal of Clinical Psychiatry* **57**: 360-3.

Department for Culture, Media and Sport (2006) *A literature review and survey of statistical sources on remote gambling*. London: DCMS.

Department for Culture, Media and Sport (2001) *Gambling Review Body Report.*[5] London: DCMS.

Griffiths MD (1993) Fruit machine gambling: the importance of structural characteristics. *Journal of Gambling Studies* **9**: 101-20.

---

5   This report, *Gambling Review Body Report* (DCMS, 2001), is commonly referred to as the Budd Report, as it was authored by the Gambling Review Body, the Chairman of which was Sir Alan Budd.

Griffiths MD (1994a) The role of cognitive bias and skill in fruit machine gambling. *British Journal of Psychology* **85**: 351-69.

Griffiths MD (1994b) An exploratory study of gambling cross addictions. *Journal of Gambling Studies* **10**: 371-84.

Griffiths MD (1994c) Co-existent fruit machine addiction and solvent abuse in adolescence: A cause for concern? *Journal of Adolescence* **17**: 491-98.

Griffiths MD (1995) *Adolescent gambling.* London: Routledge.

Griffiths MD (1996) Pathological gambling and its treatment. *British Journal of Clinical Psychology* **35**: 477-79.

Griffiths MD (1999) Gambling technologies: Prospects for problem gambling. *Journal of Gambling Studies* **15**: 265-83.

Griffiths MD (2001a) Gambling – an emerging area of concern for health psychologists. *Journal of Health Psychology* **6**: 477-79.

Griffiths MD (2001b) Internet gambling: Preliminary results of the first UK prevalence study. *Journal of Gambling Issues* **5**. Located at: www.camh.net/egambling

Griffiths MD (2002a) *Gambling and gaming addictions in adolescence.* Leicester: British Psychological Society/Blackwells.

Griffiths MD (2002b) Internet gambling in the workplace. In: Anandarajan M & Simmers C (eds) *Managing web usage in the workplace: A social, ethical and legal perspective.* Hershey, Pennsylvania: Idea Publishing.

Griffiths MD (2003a) Problem gambling. *The Psychologist: Bulletin of the British Psychological Society* **16**: 582-84.

Griffiths MD (2003b) Adolescent gambling: Risk factors and implications for prevention, intervention, and treatment. In: Romer D (ed.) *Reducing adolescent risk: Toward an integrated approach.* London: Sage.

Griffiths MD (2003c) Internet gambling: Issues, concerns and recommendations. *CyberPsychology and Behavior* **6**: 557-68.

Griffiths MD (2004) Betting your life on it. *British Medical Journal* **329**: 1055-6.

Griffiths MD (2005a) Remote gambling: Psychosocial aspects. In: *Remote Gambling* (Westminster eForum Seminar Series). London: Westminster Forum Projects Ltd.

Griffiths MD (2005b) Gambling and crime in the workplace: will it be a growing problem? *Justice of the Peace* **169**: 188-9.

Griffiths MD (2005c) A 'components' model of addiction within a biopsychosocial framework. *Journal of Substance Use* **10**: 191-7.

Griffiths MD (2005d) Online therapy for addictive behaviours. *CyberPsychology and Behavior* **8**: 555-61.

Griffiths MD (2005e) Does advertising of gambling increase gambling addiction? *International Journal of Mental Health and Addiction* **3**: 15-25.

Griffiths MD (2006) Pathological gambling. In: Plante T (ed) *Mental Disorders of the New Millennium (Volume 1: Behavioral Issues)*. New York: Greenwood.

Griffiths MD & Barnes A (2005) Internet gambling: An online empirical study among gamblers. Paper presented at the 6th European Association for the Study of Gambling Conference, July, Malmo, Sweden.

Griffiths MD, Bellringer P & Farrell-Roberts K et al (2001) Treating problem gamblers: A residential therapy approach. *Journal of Gambling Studies* **17**: 161-9.

Griffiths MD & Cooper G (2003) Online therapy: Implications for problem gamblers and clinicians. *British Journal of Guidance and Counselling* **13**: 113-35.

Griffiths MD & Delfabbro P (2001) The biopsychosocial approach to gambling: Contextual factors in research and clinical interventions. *Journal of Gambling Issues* **5**: 1-33. Located at: www.camh.net/egambling

Griffiths MD & MacDonald HF (1999) Counselling in the treatment of pathological gambling: An overview. *British Journal of Guidance and Counselling* **27**: 179-90.

Griffiths MD & Parke J (2002) The social impact of internet gambling. *Social Science Computer Review* **20**: 312-20.

Griffiths MD & Parke J (2003) The environmental psychology of gambling. In: Reith G (ed) *Gambling: Who wins? Who loses?* New York: Prometheus Books.

Griffiths MD, Parke J & Wood RTA (2002) Excessive gambling and substance abuse: is there a relationship? *Journal of Substance Abuse* **7**: 187-90.

Griffiths MD, Parke A & Wood RTA et al (2006) Internet gambling: an overview of psychosocial impacts. *Gaming Research and Review Journal* **27**: 27-39.

Griffiths MD, Scarfe A & Bellringer P (1999) The UK National telephone Helpline – results on the first year of operation. *Journal of Gambling Studies* **15**: 83-90.

Griffiths MD & Sutherland I (1998) Adolescent gambling and drug use. *Journal of Community and Applied Social Psychology* **8**: 423-7.

Hayer T, Griffiths MD & Meyer G (2005) The prevention and treatment of problem gambling in adolescence. In: Gullotta TP & Adams G (eds) *Handbook of adolescent behavioural problems: Evidence-based approaches to prevention and treatment*. New York: Springer.

Jacobs DR, Marston AR & Singer AR et al (1989) Children of problem gamblers. *Journal of Gambling Behaviour* **5**: 261-7.

Lesieur H (1988) Altering the DSM-III Criteria for pathological gambling. *Journal of Gambling Behaviour* **4**: 38-47.

Lesieur HR & Blume SB (1987) The South Oaks Gambling Screen (SOG): a new instrument for the identification of pathological gamblers. *American Journal of Psychiatry* **144**: 1184-8.

Lesieur HR & Rothschild (1989) Children of Gamblers Anonymous members. *Journal of Gambling Behaviour* **5**: 269-81.

Loughnan T, Pierce M & Sagris A (1997) *The Maroondah Assessment Profile for Problem Gambling (G-Map&trade): a new direction in problem gambling counseling.* Paper presented at the Tenth International Conference on Gambling and Risk-Taking, June, Montreal, Canada.

MORI/International Gaming Research Unit (2006) *Under 16s and the National Lottery.* London: National Lottery Commission.

Parke A, Griffiths MD & Irwing P (2004) Personality traits in pathological gambling: Sensation seeking, deferment of gratification and competitiveness as risk factors. *Addiction Research and Theory* **12**: 201-12.

Parke J & Griffiths MD (2006) The psychology of the fruit machine: the role of structural characteristics (revisited). *International Journal of Mental Health and Addiction* **4**: 151-79.

Parke J & Griffiths MD (in press) The role of structural characteristics in gambling. In: Smith G, Hodgins D & Williams R (eds), *Research and Measurement Issues in Gambling Studies.* New York: Elsevier.

Rosenthal RJ (1989) *Compulsive gambling.* Paper presented at the California Society for the Treatment of Alcoholism and Other Drug Dependencies, November, San Diego.

Rosenthal RJ & Lesieur HR (1992) Self-reported withdrawal symptoms and pathological gambling. *American Journal of the Addictions* **1**: 150-4.

Sproston K, Erens B & Orford J (2000) *Gambling Behaviour in Britain, Results from the British Gambling Prevalence Survey.* London: National Centre For Social Research.

Shaffer HJ, Hall MN & Vander Bilt J (1999) Estimating the prevalence of disordered gambling behaviour in the United States and Canada: a research synthesis. *American Journal of Public Health* **89**: 1369-76.

Shaffer HJ, LaBrie RA & LaPlante D (2004) Laying the foundation for quantifying regional exposure to social phenomena: considering the case of legalized gambling as a public health toxin. *Psychology of Addictive Behaviors* **18**: 40-8.

Smeaton M & Griffiths MD (2004) Internet gambling and social responsibility: an exploratory study. *CyberPsychology and Behavior* **7**: 49-57.

National Gambling Impact Study Commission (1999) *Final report.* Washington, DC: Government Printing Office.

Volberg RA (1996) Prevalence studies of problem gambling in the United States. *Journal of Gambling Studies* **12**: 111-28.

Volberg RA (2001) *When the chips are down: problem gambling in America*. New York, NY: The Century Foundation.

Walker MB (1992) *The Psychology of Gambling*. New York, NY: Permagon.

Ward P (2004) *The Gambling Bill (Research Paper 04/79)*. London: House of Commons.

Wood RTA & Griffiths MD (1998) The acquisition, development and maintenance of lottery and scratchcard gambling in adolescence. *Journal of Adolescence* **21**: 265-73.

Wood RTA (2004) Adolescent lottery and scratchcard players: do their attitudes influence their gambling behaviour? *Journal of Adolescence* **27**: 467-75.

Wood RTA, Griffiths MD & Parke J (in press) The acquisition, development, and maintenance of online poker playing in a student sample. *CyberPsychology and Behaviour.*

Yeoman T & Griffiths MD (1996) Adolescent machine gambling and crime. *Journal of Adolescence* **19**: 183-8.

Department of Science and Education publications

- Selection for specialty training (2006)
- Doctors as teachers (2006)
- Child and adolescent mental health: a guide for healthcare professionals (2006)
- Reporting adverse drug reactions: a guide for healthcare professionals (2006)
- Tackling sexually transmitted infections – examples of good practice (2006)
- Sexually transmitted infections update 2006 – in light of new figures from HPA (2006)
- Healthcare associated infections – a guide for healthcare professionals (2006)
- Becoming a doctor 2007 (web resource – updated annually)
- Interprofessional Education (2006)
- Medical women – an internet resource (2006)
- Examining Equality – a survey of royal college examinations (2006)
- The expert patients programme – a discussion paper (2005)
- Guide to effective communication – non-discriminatory language (2005)
- Sexual orientation in the workplace (2005)
- Religion and belief: best practice guide for arranging meetings (2005)
- Medical specialties: the way forward (2005)
- Population and genetic screening (2005)
- Vaccine development – web resource (2005)
- Mobile phones and health – an update (2005)
- Healthcare in a rural setting (2005)
- Sexually Transmitted infections update 2005 – in light of new figures from HPA (2005)
- Binge drinking (2005)
- Emergency planning arrangements for the NHS in the UK – a collection of responses from the Board of Science (2005)
- Hepatitis B vaccination in childhood (2005)
- Over the counter medication (2005)
- Preventing childhood obesity (2005)
- Biotechnology, weapons and humanity II (2004)
- Sexually transmitted infections: an update (2004)
- Refuse management and health (2004)
- The impact of flying on passenger health: a guide for healthcare professionals (2004)
- Genetically modified foods and health: a second interim statement (2004)
- Medical education A to Z 2004 (web resource)
- Developing the doctor – manager leadership role (2004)
- Diabetes mellitus: an update for healthcare professionals (2004)
- Smoking and reproductive life: the impact on smoking, reproductive and child health (2004)
- Valuing diversity: BMA equal opportunities guidelines (2004)
- Exploring mentoring (2004)
- Career barriers in medicine: doctors' experiences (2004)
- The demography of medical schools: a discussion paper (2004)

Copies of these and other reports can be obtained from:
Science and Education Department, British Medical Association,
BMA House, Tavistock Square, London, WC1H 9JP.
Tel: +44 (0) 20 7383 6164 Fax: +44 (0) 20 7383 6383
Email: info.science@bma.org.uk
www.bma.org.uk